Comfort zone are boring. It's time to...

#do

the

thing

Dona Sarkar

Everyone's got that thing.

Yes, even you. You know what I'm talking about. Your secret dream or idea. Maybe you haven't yet started to make it a reality...but you can't stop thinking about it.

Why haven't you started yet?

Maybe it's because you don't have time.

Maybe it's because you don't know how to start.

Maybe it's because you have no one to talk to about it to see if it even makes sense.

Maybe there is someone in your life who's going to raise an eyebrow of disapproval.

Maybe it's because it's simply too "big" of a dream for someone like you to tackle right now.

Maybe it's because it's too late. You've already chosen and gone down a path.

Maybe it's because you have achieved everything you set out to when you were young. A lot of people have this notion that if you are "successful"—that if you have the house, the car, the family, the friends, the vacation—then you must surely be happy and deeply fulfilled with your life. Right?

Maybe it's something else that's holding you back. Maybe you can't even formulate into words what exactly you're trying to do. But you know you're meant to do more than *this*.

I have a feeling you're in one of these categories otherwise you wouldn't be reading this book right now.

Why do I know this?

Because this is NORMAL.

In August of 2017, I realized I was having the same conversation over and over again with people who had achieved everything they had set out to do when they were younger and now...they were stuck.

"I want to do more...but I don't want to waste my time. I have so much other stuff going on."

I have been a fiction writer for many years and often when I'm stuck, I have put myself into one of my stories and figured out my next step by removing my real-life biases from the equation. I had a theory that my stuck friends could do this too. By putting themselves into the shoes of a fictional version of themselves, they would be able to figure out their next thing and then take the necessary steps to actually do the thing.

However, I needed to test this theory on some real humans.

I put out a call on LinkedIn: *Anyone who is feeling this way, please gather on Thursday in <a specified room> in <a specified building> in Seattle and let's figure this out together.*

I was convinced no one was going to show up. To my surprise, 25 people showed up. To my even greater surprise, after a bit of silence where everyone did the 3rd person journaling activity I asked them to do, people started authentically and vulnerably sharing what they were seeking in their lives.

This led to us gathering for 4 more weeks and forming an online #DoTheThing community. The community is still vibrant and active today and is looking for people like YOU to join us. Come say hi to us at
https://www.facebook.com/groups/DoTheThingYo

We all realized we have something in common. We all have great lives. Ideal lives, in fact. Lives most people in the world would give anything for. We have jobs that pay well, families we love, and we are healthy people. But still...there is a restlessness within. There is that whisper that we know all too well.

Is this all there is?

NO. This is NOT all there is.

In the community, we went through the same set of exercises you will all of us in the sessions had revelations, realizations and took actions to accept this whisper—this *call of adventure.*

Our #DoTheThing community members (and by holding this book, you are now one of us, BTW) are not the exception. Today you are going to take step one (well, maybe not TODAY today, but pretty soon here) to understand that call of adventure and walk toward it (instead of away from it—that would defeat the purpose of doing the thing). And you're going to do it in an organized, safe way that won't be as scary as it seems.

Trust me.

You are not alone. This is a global problem. Therefore, you have a global community of people in the same boat. I'm one of them. We are all here to help you, talk through things with you, not judge you and generally have your back. If you're struggling at

any point during this exercise, come share with us at
https://www.facebook.com/groups/DoTheThingYo

This is a closed group, so no outside judgement is allowed. Our group exists to support and nurture one another's dreams because we are NOT alone in how we feel. It sounds super new-agey, but it works.

We're building this community as we speak and by reading this book, YOU are a key member of it!

Look, you've been waiting too long to do this. No one ever looked back and said, "Well, good thing I waited so long to fulfill that thing I really wanted to do!"

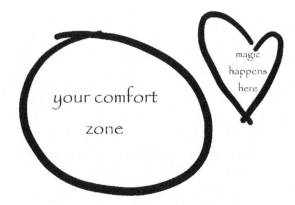

By the end of this book, you are going to get out of your comfort zone. Remember, if magic was going to strike in your comfort zone, it probably would have happened by now. Let's go make that magic happen.

We got this. Let's go #DoTheThing – together.

The Hero's Journey

Have you noticed that it's always easier to give advice to other people and help them solve their problems rather than our own? However, if we are facing the EXACT same problem, we freeze in fear and doubt even though the advice might be the same. We tend to not be overly critical or doubtful with our friends. Instead, we're supportive and helpful (otherwise, they probably wouldn't be our friends). We are not nearly as kind or as patient with ourselves.

Why we do this?

Doesn't matter. It's time to end this cycle.

We're going to debug ourselves and our goals using some ancient fiction writing techniques, namely the concept called The Hero's Journey. This structure is used in most books and movies. It takes our protagonist through a bunch of stages to help them understand their current situation, build their tribe, learn some skills, overcome their villains and achieve their goals.

Just go with it. It'll make sense soon.

Let's explore the Hero's Journey in four acts.

ACT 1: The Ordinary World – this is the introduction to our hero's current life (or heroine, of course but for the sake of simplicity, we will refer to this human as "hero"). It involves understanding how they spend their time, who they roll with, what their strengths are and what they value.

ACT II: The Call of Adventure – this is where our hero goes on a self-discovery mission to figure out what is the "thing" they are supposed to be doing.

ACT III: Refusal of the Call - this is where our hero is a giant chicken or is held back by something that can be overcome. They need to discover what is holding them back and then overcome it.

ACT IV: Do The Thing - this is where our hero emerges as well, the hero of this story and does what they are supposed to be doing.

Confused yet? Let's walk through the story of a friend of ours, Amy Nelson, the CEO and founder of The Riveter to showcase these stages:

The Ordinary World: Amy had spent over 10 years as a corporate litigator in New York, Minneapolis and eventually Seattle. She also worked in political fundraising, had served on President Obama's National Finance Committee and was a cofounder of Gen44, the President's under-40 fundraising arm. She had a wonderful, supportive husband, liked her job and was good at it.

The Call of Adventure: Once her first child was born, she realized that there was enormous potential in sleep consultation of babies. She'd always wanted to run her own business, so she started going to various local co-working spaces to attend classes on how to write business plans and raise funds. While she appreciated these spaces, she didn't find them to be a good place to network with other women entrepreneurs.
She realized there was a huge opportunity for her to create a co-working space that was designed for women, but was welcoming to men. This idea kept coming back to her. Imagine, a place for women anywhere in their careers, a community of supportive professional women with a focus on overall health and wellness.

Refusal of the Call: At this point, Amy had a young child at home, was pregnant with another child AND had a full-time job. Opening a physical space was going to be an expensive and a completely all- encompassing endeavor. She spoke with a friend about the idea of opening one co-working space. He looked at her in disbelief and said, "Why are you opening one? You should open 100!" She realized that not only was her idea not crazy, but she needed to think BIGGER.

Do The Thing: Since then, Amy has raised enough money to open two locations of The Riveter (in Capitol Hill and Fremont in Seattle) and is working on several more locations in San Francisco, LA, Texas and Bellevue, Washington, leveraging her years of fund-raising experience. Oh, and she has three little girls under the age of 5 at home. Her newborn accompanies her to many fundraising meetings as well as our interview!

Before the doors of the first Riveter space officially opened and was still in a state of partial construction, Amy received the opportunity to host Sheryl Sandberg's book launch of Option B. She of course, did the thing and said YES.

Her advice to us was simple: make a plan—but don't make it perfect. We hold ourselves back by wanting to have all our ducks in a row, a finalized plan, all unknowns known. Starting a business is sometimes an exercise is being okay with 70% "great"—and trusting that you'll figure out the 30% on the way.

One example from our #DoTheThing community is someone who decided that she was done watching politics unfold from the sidelines and decided to run for City Council to make true change happen. Another was someone who decided that he was going to write that book on "Neuroscience for Non-scientists" that he realizes the world needs. I, personally, overcame my fear of needles and judgment, flew halfway around the world to Australia to get a tattoo of a quill and a clock to remind myself that my writing time is precious, and time is the one thing I cannot create more of.

The world is full of people who are "doing the thing". They are fitting many lives into this one. And today, you are going to join them.

You Ready?

It's your turn. In the next 80ish pages, you're going to write a Hero's Journey story.

The hero in the story is you up to this point in your life, but you are going to tell the story as the author. You're going to use the 3rd person point-of-view of an omnipresent narrator who can feel and see all, but is NOT in the hero's body.

In our #DoTheThing sessions, being the author has been the big unblocker for people—to remove the "them" from the equation. This will help you make your writing more factual with less of a "you" bias. It might feel very weird at first, then you'll get used to it and find yourself able to look at your life in a much more objective way.

To help kickstart thinking, we've included some of my own real-life examples in *italics*. If you truly take the time to do this AND are honest with yourself, you will have a lot more clarity in the next few hours, days, weeks, months...however long it takes you to go through this process. We have tested this method on many humans, which is why this book exists.

You're going to read about many concepts in this book that you have heard before. However, how many times have you taken the time to write down your next steps and then DO them? Do yourself a favor and do the work. It will pay off, trust us. The more you put in, the more you will get from your investment.

This means that over the course of the next few days and weeks, you're going to need to make some time to do the exercises in this book with your hero in mind. We recommend 20-minute blocks when you can find some place to be alone, to put your phone across the room and set a timer for 20 minutes. There is something magical about setting a timer. This Pomodoro Technique was introduced to us by our member Philippe Brissaud and it has been a huge hit to just go without letting our neurotic brains talk us out of it. The goal here is to not edit yourself and race to get done as much as possible in 20 mins.

You will also need a blank journal or notebook that you will write even more words in. Yes, you can type them, but we have seen tremendous success in physically writing things down without the distractions of email or social media notifications. Suddenly, the words you write go from being vague ideas to real goals. Suddenly, your brain is no longer filtering out things relating to these ideas and instead is highlighting them. Think about the phenomenon that when you buy a specific car, you suddenly see that car everywhere. There are not more cars. The filter is just removed for you.

Suddenly, the things you write down become real.

Side note: This just happened to me. I wrote down in my journal a goal to meet a certain person who works in venture capital. I looked at the agenda for a conference I'm attending soon and lo and behold, she's going to be there speaking as well.

You can write the exercise answers in this book or in your journal. Totally up to you. In our #DoTheThing class, it was an even split.

When completing these exercises, you need to be 100% honest for best results. Remember, NO ONE is going to see this journal or these exercises (unless you want to show people). They are between you and your hero, so leave your judgement of your hero at the door. They trust you to help them get through this journey.

Okay, ready? We are going to do the Mel Robbins 5 Second Rule rule....
Don't think. Don't hesitate. Just flip the page and go. Ready?

5-4-3-2-1 GO!

Act I: The Ordinary World

The hero of my story is named

You can name them after yourself, a nickname or something else entirely. Someone once named their hero The King of Catnip-town, so...name them and let's get into their Ordinary World.

The Ordinary World is well, your hero's ordinary world. It's the life they currently have, the one where something seems amiss. It's incredibly important to understand their world and their role in it well before we try to introduce something potentially scary into it. What are the things currently in their head? Where does their time go? Next, it's important to understand who their tribe is. Who are the humans who will be with them throughout their journey? Then we must understand what their "core" is, so they can continue to maximize on their strengths as they take on the new thing.

In our #DoTheThing sessions, we notice that people really struggle to write down what they're proud of and what their strengths are. This is one of the reasons we are writing about ourselves from the point of view of an omnipresent narrator. This is also a very good time to lean on the people in your hero's life that depend on them. Often, our hero is their own worst critic and can't spot their superpowers.

Why is your hero re-evaluating their life now? What are some things that have happened recently that has led your hero to pause from their busy life and invest in themselves now?

My example is: *Ananya is realizing that her greatest happiness comes when she can help people achieve something they didn't realize they were craving. She loves "pushing people out of the plane" and being an enabler. Her issue is that her time is* filled up with things that do not bring her this level of happiness. Something has to change. She has to find a way to make the thing she loves to do a part of her day-to-day life.

Write yours here:

Journaling

Let's start the journaling! All existing journalers are like "yaaaay, homework!" All non-journalers are rolling their eyes. Trust me, this is going to be fun. I thought journaling was dumb, but now I must journal a few days a week to feel like I have a good grasp on my life.

There have been hundreds of studies that show that journaling is a very good way to get worries and intentions out of our brains and onto paper, so we can parse it, rather than keep it tangled up in our heads. I love all articles by Benjamin Hardy, especially the one titled: "How I use my journal to create my future and achieve my goals". He points out that most creators keep journals including super legit people like Mark Twain, George Lucas, Beethoven, Hemingway, Marie Curie, Frida Kahlo. You get the point. Give it a shot.

I became a major believer in journaling after I started using his technique. The sheer amount of clarity I got from following this method lead to me writing not just this book, but start my next one in quick succession while maintaining performance in my day job and my social life.

Grab that journal or notebook and do the following for at least a few days this week. Remember, no one is going to see this. The key is not to overthink, process or edit.

Just write the first 5 things that come to mind.
1.   Write down the date.
2.   Write down 3-5 things your hero is grateful for. Don't get too philosophical. Just 5 great things in your hero's life. Remember, they have a life that mirrors yours, so everyone and everything in your life, they have too. *Example: Ananya is grateful to have a friend like Kristina, with who she can have a 5-minute conversation and feel like*

she's not actually crazy. Ananya is grateful for that one hour today when everyone went the heck away and gave her a few minutes to herself.

3.   Write down something your hero is proud of themselves for doing the previous day. *Example: Ananya is proud of not calling you-know-who on his bullshit and having a long argument because, seriously, who has the time for that?*

4.   Write down 3-5 things that are worrying your hero or stressing them out. They don't need to be major. Just things that are weighing on your hero's mind. *Example: Ananya is worried that being in the road for 10 days is hard on her team at work*

At this point, you might feel compelled to write solutions to these worries the hero has. If so, do it. This is your problem-solving muscle kicking in. Notice it's easier see solutions to problems when they are written in someone else's point of view. *Example: Before Ananya leaves for her trip, she should schedule check in calls with the team every few days and then keep in touch with them via text so they can let her know in real time if anything goes wrong.*

If you suddenly feel like writing more stuff, do that. Your hero's dreams. Ideas. Fears. Anything. This is your subconscious trying to tell you something. Take the time to write this down. Be free and uninhibited with your thoughts since no one will see them. Get them down on paper so you can see them.

Time Check

We spend time as if we have endless amounts of it. We give much more thought to how we spend money, compared to how we spend time...even though we can make more money, but we can never make more time. Let's start being deliberate about where your hero's time goes.

In the journal or a spreadsheet, make 5 columns marked as follows and fill it in hour by hour for a minimum of 2 days. Start at your hero's normal wake-up time. Remember that no one is seeing this, but you so be very honest about what brings your hero joy and what does not.

I've added some of my own hero's entries as examples in the table below.

Time	Activity	Negative/ Neutral/ Positive Mood	Mandatory?	Notes - what she did, how she felt
4:00 am	read articles she saved	Positive	No	motivating articles put her in a great "do the thing" mood
5:00 am	Plan the day, think about the team	Positive	Yes	She got rid of some meetings and made more time to spend with the team
6:00 am	Read twitter + email & reply	Negative	No	Why does she start the day with this? She needs to not do this till she gets to work. Email is people needing things and Twitter is just...wow. This can wait till work.

Annotate things on this sheet that are:
a) not absolutely mandatory for living AND
b) things that are negative or neutral

Now you need to help your hero reduce the time they spend on things that don't make them feel positive and are not absolutely mandatory. We can guarantee there are some things on your list that can go, and no one will notice.

One technique someone in a #DoTheThing session did was stop doing almost everything except their core day job and observed if anyone noticed. To their surprise, no one cared that they didn't attend every single meeting and event they were invited to or respond to every single email. The world did not fall down and in fact, they were able to find enough time to work on a long-brewing passion project.

You absolutely need to make room in your hero's life before you introduce new things in. It's like having a full bookshelf of books you don't love. You can't get new books that you truly love till you make room.

What are some things you would advise your hero to reduce spending time on to make room for the thing they are going to introduce into their world?
For Ananya, it was email and Twitter. She is spending hours throughout the day on email and Twitter for work. None of it brought her any joy or happiness.

What are some concrete steps you would advise your hero to take? Here was my advice to my hero:

Yo Ananya, do this:
- Uninstall work email from your phone
- Check only three times a day: morning after you get to work, afternoon, and again in the evening before going home. Do not look on weekends till Sunday night.
- Keep Twitter to only three times a day since it's part of the day job. Move the Twitter app to the last page into a folder where you'll never look

I have now done this for 4 months. The world did not end. Everyone who needs to get a hold of me urgently knows to text me. I did not miss out on anything of significance.

Write down your instructions to your hero and then take these actions in your own life.

Who is going to hold your hero accountable? Write them a note right now telling them you are counting on them to help you do this. There is something so much more official about getting an email or other written word about being responsible for something.

What are some things in the time list that bring your hero a lot of joy that you want them to keep doing or do more of?

How exactly are they going to do that? What are the concrete steps they will take to make time and energy to do those things?

Again, who is going to hold you accountable to make sure you and your hero are doing this? Let them know!

The Tribe

Every hero has a tribe of people who help them on their journey. These are the worldly mentors who say smart things, the pushy coaches who make them run stairs 80 times, the ridiculous side-kick who offers comic relief, the resourceful nerd who helps makes tools.

It's time for your hero to discover and/or build their tribe.

<3

Who are some people who really believed in your hero when they were young? A teacher? A coach? A friend? Write their names here.

What did they do to make your hero feel this way?

How did their belief in your hero make your hero feel?

Who in your hero's life makes them feel that way today?

Is there someone in your hero's life who truly wants the best for them no matter what?
Someone who TRULY wants them to achieve all their dreams no matter how crazy?
Who?
(If you don't have this person, come talk to us in the #DoTheThing group. We are
ALL people who are willing to do this for and with you.)

Who are the people your hero does this for?

Now, think about people your hero admires. They are people who embody the kind of characteristics they would like to build or build more within themselves. These do not have to be people with who they interact with daily—just people they admire. It can be people they stalk on Instagram!

Write down at least 3 people.

Humans my hero admires and what the characteristics they admire are...

Human	Thing I admire about them
Alice	Always optimistic and positive no matter how hard things get. Always ready to help solve a problem no matter how much "not her problem" it is. She is an enabler and pushes me to think bigger.

Who are some people who depend on your hero regularly? This can be family, friends, co-workers, whoever.

Write down who they are and what they depend on your hero for.

Human	Thing they depend on your hero for
Brandon	Give him aircover at work

If you have been doing the gratitude journaling (which you should be!), have there been repeat characters who have shown up that your hero is grateful for? Write their names down here.

Who are the happiest people your hero knows in real life?

Who are some people your hero knows who love to learn?

Okay, now, have a look at the all the names you wrote down in the above sections. How many of those people are reachable—as in they are alive and not super-famous, and you think you can reach out to?

You are the average of the five people who influence you the most, so you and your hero should be influenced by people you admire and aspire to be like. You need to make room in your hero's life to spend with these people rather than people who drain you. These folks need to become members of your tribe.

Write your Tribe members names down here (3-5 is great if possible):
1.

2.

3.

4.

5.

What do these people have in common (if anything)?

Next, do one or both of the following:

If you haven't not already, make plans to spend more time with some of the people above who inspire you in the next few weeks, or at least do a voice call of some sort. You don't need to tell them what you are doing, but we have found that surrounding ourselves with people who are positive influences has a pretty magical effect in our lives.

Next to each name, write down how you'll spend time with them this month.

Write them a note telling them a very specific way they have influenced you. You can use the words you wrote above.

Seriously, no matter how famous or busy someone is, they never get enough praise. For every good comment, people receive 100 times or more negative messages.

Something simple like this works amazingly well:

Dear <human>

I'm doing an exercise to think about my motivations and goals. One of the exercises asked me to write down people I admire and what I admire about them. You are one of mine and here is what I wrote. <your thing here>

Thank you for being you. I know it's not always easy. I hope you know how much of an impact you've had on me.

This will absolutely make their day. Trust me on this one. For everyone nice comment people get, there are 1000 negative comments. Send the nice note.

The Core

Now, let's investigate the core of who your hero is. These are the fundamental truths about them that will likely not change. Their values, their strengths and their aspirations.

Look at the common traits among your hero's Tribe members answer above. These are the things your hero wants to embody no matter what "job" they are doing. These are some of their **Values**.

Some of my hero's Values are:
1. *Believing anything is possible*

2.

3.

4.

This is a list of things you want your hero to BE more of or DO more of.

Look again at how your hero spends their time. What are some activities your hero should remove from the timesheet because they are not contributing to living per their values?

Now what are some activities your hero should add to make sure they are living their values?

Next let's talk about your hero's **Strengths**.

Hardships and recovery really show a person's strengths. Think about a time in your hero's life when they faced hardship. When things were just not good, and they felt quite helpless. Write down what was the hardship and how they coped and recovered from it.

Hardship	How they coped and recovered
Being laid off from first job	Called on network
	Studied tech every day
	Worked on novel to maintain control over one part of their life— which later got published!

For this next part, find 3 people in your hero's life (potentially from the "who depends on you" list and reach out to them. Ask them the question, "What would you call me for help with?" Do reach out and ask people, don't just make this up. In our sessions, more than one person was VERY surprised at what people would call on them for.

I've noticed that people call on my hero to help with...

1.

2.

3.

How do these line up with what you thought they would say?

Some things that my hero has done that they are proud of are (again, if you're stuck, ask someone you've listed above)

1. In the past week...

2. In the past month...

3. In the past year...

4.   In the past 3 years...

5.   In their life...

Looking at these lists, it becomes obvious that some of my hero's strengths are:

1.

2.

3.

4.

5.

It's super important that we focus on the areas where not only are we strong, but also confident. Think about when your hero feels the most alive and at the top of their game.

My hero is the most confident when...

1.

2.

3.

Write about a time that your hero felt incredibly powerful. Think about who they were interacting with. What specific activities they were doing. Why did they feel powerful, what was the **outcome** that occurred that made them feel powerful?

Look at the list of people your hero has in their tribe as well as who depends on them.

If any of those people were to talk about your hero, what words would you WANT them to describe your hero as?

What patterns are emerging? What are the repeated words or phrases. Circle or annotate them in some way. These are a part of your hero's brand. These are the things your hero should keep doing as much as possible to turn these into superpowers.

Go back to the timesheet and figure out who to add in more of these kinds of activities. Mark them as "Mandatory" because they are.

And that's all for now! Intense, huh?

Before we move on, let's look back at your Ordinary World. Turns out there is nothing ordinary about it. This is REAL. This is the life you and your hero have created 100% with your own choices.

Be proud of what you have done. Be proud of the amazing person you are and all that you have overcome. **Accept yourself and your life you have built because it's the only way to become MORE of what you want.**

Act II: The Call of Adventure

Hear that?

That's adventure and possibilities calling your hero's name. Now that we have a good idea of who this human is, we can figure out what they want next.

Now, don't get all resist-ey, like "they don't have time" or "they have too many responsibilities" or "they don't have money". You are writing fiction. Anything is possible in fiction-land. If authors always stuck to the hero's ordinary world, Dorothy would still be hiding out in the house waiting for another tornado to take her home, Diana wouldn't be Wonder Woman, instead she'd be hanging out being all strong on that Amazonian island. Bruce Wayne would be like, "Whatevs, this job and being rich lifestyle is fine".

The Ordinary World is comfortable, but the inevitable next step is that adventure will call, and the hero must answer.

You got this book for a reason and your hero is going to at least explore the options. They don't need to DO anything. They just need to know what more is out there in this great big world. Remember, writing things down doesn't make it a mandatory thing they need to do.

We are also not going to get hung up on "finding your passion". Very few people know what they are passionate about until they are passionate about it. In our experience, your hero will end up passionate about something once they

a) try it
b) get kind of good at it and
c) like it

So, generally it takes a bit of time, and maybe a few attempts to develop a passion for something.

Many times, heroes don't know what they want. They do know what they are currently struggling with. Something that keeps them up at night. What are some things your hero has been thinking about lately that are reoccurring? Things that keep coming back over and over in their worries. Things that they might be struggling with.

Write them down and out of your hero's head so that you have some free space to create the next adventure.

Things on my hero's mind are...

Now go take a break. Get a cup of something. Walk around. Put some dishes away. Something short. 15 mins max.

My husband always knows I'm writing when random bits of housework mysteriously gets done.

When you come back, you the author are going to try and help the hero find solutions to the problems they have listed.

I, the author and ultimate omnipresent being of this story, advise you to....

How is the journaling going? Still doing gratitudes and worries? It's a great way to get a bit of time to yourself and your mind on the daily. Have a look through at your previous worries. How are you feeling about them now? In my case, the things I worried about 2 weeks ago never became a thing that caused me much stress. I just had to get them out of my head.

Here is another activity to add to it. Start keep an "Idea List". Whenever an idea comes to you, either practical or potentially stupid, just write it down. Don't edit. Just keep a running list in your journal. Remember: no one is seeing this!

Stream of Consciousness

Now, in this next section, without thinking too much, you will answer the following questions.

It's highly important that your hero doesn't obsess about the HOW right now. Just write down the "whats", not the "hows". We'll work through the "how" in a whole different chapter. Absolutely fine if some of the questions don't resonate or your hero gets stuck. Leave them and move on.

Now, set the timer for 20 mins. Put your phone across the room.

No, really though, do it.

In 10 years, my hero will be _____ years old. 5 items on their Bucket List to do before then are

1.

2.

3.

4.

5.

In 20 years, my hero will be _____ years old. 5 or more items on their Bucket List to do before then are:

Write down 3 things in your hero's life that other people have tried that looked or sounded interesting to them and who was the person who did this:

1.

2.

3.

Of the names written above, did any of the people have special, magical powers that they were born with? Or did they become special because of what they did? How did they manage to do this activity? How did they learn? Can you ask them (or one of their employees or mentees) about what their step 1 was? **Write down their step one next to the activity they did.**

Imagine that your hero is reborn as the same person without money being a concern.

How would they spend their days? List 3 things.

1.

2.

3.

What are some common themes among these activities?

Who are some people they would want in their life in this other life? List 3 people.

1.

2.

3.

What are the values those people embody (values exercise from Act 1)?

1.

2.

3.

Okay, let's come back to this lifetime. What would 3 things your hero would attempt if there was zero chance of failure or them looking stupid?

1.

2.

3.

What are 3 things your hero liked to do when they were younger, but gave them up?

1.

2.

3.

What was something your hero missed out on the chance to do when they were younger?

What are some things your hero would like to try if they had more time right now?

1.

2.

3.

If your hero had one day to spend on themselves with ZERO obligations, would that look like for them?

How about a week?

How about a month?

Okay, imagine that the thing your hero spends their days doing...that job/role/activity is gone. Like it disappears from the planet. Write an alternate life for your hero. Fill in details. What would their days be full of? Who would they spend time with?

We are now going to do an activity to find your hero's ANDs. Where an AND lies, you can be an influencer. As my friend and role model Kristina Libby says, an influencer is someone who has experience and credibility in two or more worlds. They are able to influence people in one field with their knowledge of the other. We will do this based on your hero's strengths.

Ananya's AND is fashion design, tech and fiction writing. She is not the best fashion designer, coder or writer in the world. However, she is a more credible fashion designer than most coders and a more credible coder than most fashion designers. There is something interesting there. Now add fiction to the mix. She is definitely a more credible fiction writer and coder than most fashion designers, etc.

Her intersections look like this:

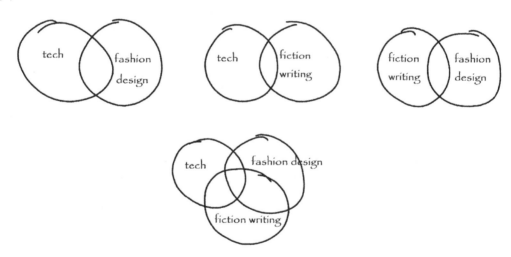

What is your hero's ANDs? Pick a combination of 2 or 3 things from the various lists above that seem sane: Keep in mind the things people call on your help for as well as the activities during your day-to-day that bring you positivity.

Now forget sane. Start putting in random things from the various lists in the circles. You are writing fiction. Imagine creating a brand-new character who is...

Keep going. Now imagine you're writing a fantasy novel. What is the most outlandish combo you can think of?

Now circle or highlight the most compelling activities on the previous pages, including the ANDs. The ones your eyes and thoughts keep coming back to. What truly excites you, thrills you, scares the heck out of you to learn more about or to solve? Where the "what if" sounds exciting (despite potentially being terrifying?)

Write those ideas down here.

1.

2.

3.

Put this book down now. Creativity is making connections between different parts of the brain. Now that your brain is thinking of different things than usual, let's give it time to do the unconscious connections thing.

Go do something that is not active consuming. Something repetitive and brainless like showering, putting dishes away, driving in a familiar place or taking a familiar walk.

Someplace where muscle memory kicks in so that you don't need to think too much.

<3

Let your mind go where it will. Does the idea of pursuing some of these things start to become a small reality with a small first step?

Write down what your hero thought of here:

Now reach out to someone who your hero would want in one of their alternate lives above and thank them for exhibiting the values you wrote down for them. You'll make their day and let your brain process what you're prioritizing. Yep, same as last time. Appreciation, appreciation, appreciation!

If you feel up to it, share with them one or more of things you circled/highlighted. What did they have to say about it? Did they seem interested to hear more?

Write about it here:

In this next part, your hero is asking you to help them incorporate the activities and ideas they wrote down above into current life.

What advice would you give them for each on the step 1. This is not how to become super-successful, but how to learn enough to know a tiny bit more. Don't think too much. Just WRITE. Remember, your hero will not actually need to DO these. This is just fiction writing.

1.

2.

3.

What is possible for your hero to do today? Don't overthink. You already know. Just highlight or mark it in some way or write it below.

Your adventure officially has a name now.

And it's calling yours.

ACT III: Refusal of the Call

Okay, this is the part of the story when the hero has a bit of a meltdown. Either they are feeling imposter syndrome, or they are coming up with reasons they don't want to or cannot do the things they listed in the previous section.

We need to help them overcome these silent villains. If they truly did not want to do the thing they marked in the previous section, they would not have written it down. They certainly would not be reading this far.

It's time for them to take step one of doing the thing.

Like, now.

And they don't need anyone's permission to do so.

We need to let go of this idea of Permission. We never used to ask for permission when we were young. We didn't ask for permission when we drew on the walls when we were 5 or took apart that remote control when we were 7.

Nope, it was adults who drilled into us this idea of permission. Grown-ups (damn them) taught us that we must ask for permission. For everything. To leave the dinner table. To ask a question in class. This system was put in place to keep us safe and not feral. Unfortunately, now as adults, we struggle to do something unless someone has given us the permission to do so.

The #DoTheThing group hate the phrase "beg for forgiveness, rather than ask for permission". Why beg for forgiveness? It's your life. Why do you need permission for? You've gotten yourself to this point, why would you not be the primary decision maker of what fulfills you? You own your time. Do with it what you will.

It's time to fulfill that promise to that surly young adult who once said, "When I grow up, I'm going to do whatever I want."

That day is today.

<3

In fiction writing, there is a concept called Goal, Motivation and Conflict that authors use to deeply understand the hero/heroine. We will use that framework to understand where the hero of *this* story is going.

You might already be making up reasons why any of the things you wrote down in the previous section don't make sense in your hero's life.

Of course, they make sense, or you wouldn't have taken the time to write them down. How often do you thoughtfully write things down just for yourself that you do not mean?

It's okay. We'll get through his together.

GOAL

What do you want to do with the ideas you wrote down above? Write a "My hero wants" statement. Remember, no one is seeing this sheet of paper. Be honest. You do not need to be very specific as in "My hero wants to be a professional chef at French Laundry" Instead, you want something that is in the general direction as in "My hero wants to learn more about what it means to be a professional chef" or "My hero wants to be more involved in the local food community"

Write yours here:

MOTIVATION

WHY does your hero want to do this? Every hero has an origins story. What's in your hero's background that compels them to want to do this? Let's take a walk through their history and find out how they arrived here. This is their Motivation.

Have they been curious about this or have tried this before?

Do they have skills in this area or in something that could be related (like they're good at teaching and they'd like to learn about this thing and then teach it to others)?

Is there someone they know who has done this or similar?

Is it just something that sounds or looks cool?

Any other reason?

There are NO wrong answers. Just a general idea of why this idea came to them.

So those are the things you will tell the world. But what is the REAL reason? The not-noble reason. The selfish reason that we never want anyone to know.

We're going to find it.

Back in the day, my writing teacher, the incredible Janet Lee Carey taught me how to discover secret motivation. Usually, this is 3-5 levels deeper than what we tell the world. In this next part, you will explore your hero's secret motivation. Don't be afraid! Remember, no one is going to see this but you. Let's do this.

Why is the thing you just wrote down in the Goals section important to the hero?

Why is the thing you just wrote on the previous page important to your hero?

Why is the thing you wrote above important to your hero? Keep digging.

Why is THAT important to your hero? It's okay if these motivations are getting less noble. It's okay if the reason is "to be remembered" or "to be important". This is very human. Go ahead. Write it here. No one will see this. I promise.

Mine turned out to be to prove the community I grew up in (people who spend a LOT of time thinking about "what people will say") and to not be forgotten. It's not noble, but it's real.

There, that wasn't so bad, right?

CONFLICT

Okay, so what is (or has been) standing in your hero's way of even starting the thing they are now thinking about? No matter how stupid, just write it. Be very honest with your hero about this. Lack of time to devote to this? Other priorities? Just realizing they want to do this now? Some sort of fear? Someone's judgement? Lack of knowledge?

Set a timer for 20 minutes. Write down from your hero's perspective of why it won't work.

A real example is this:

Ananya is afraid to start this #Do The Thing movement even though she and I both think it's a great idea. Her issues are that:
• It's going to take up a ton of time that she doesn't have to run the experiments, write the stories and write the workbook.
• She's likely going to have to let go of something she really likes to be able to focus, like fashion design
• If it becomes very useful to people, she will likely need to make a hard choice between working full time in tech and helping people do the thing.

Now write your hero's version here:

Done? Good. Go get something to drink or take a walk and take your mind off this. When you come back, set a timer for 10 minutes. It's creative brainstorming time.

Write down a time when your hero faced issues like what they wrote above. Which of the worries were overblown in the past? What did they do last time?

Write an idea or two next to each one to refute each issue from you the author's or other people's points of view.

For my hero, I wrote this to Ananya:

- For the time issue, don't look at work email at night. Use the 4-5:30 am magic hour to get writing and processing done. Start having meetings with people who need to DTT rather than the standard crew every night.
- Yo, if you were going to go all in on fashion design, you would have written it down, no? It's something you can do after. Fabric and such is just getting more and more sustainable. It will get easier, not harder to get into that industry in a year or more.
- Worry about that hard choice when it comes. You can likely hire people who's done the thing to run sessions like other training programs do.

Now go back and write advice for your hero next to each issue.

If you and your hero are struggling with this, call one of the people in the Ordinary World section and ask them for help to solve this problem. Or you can always ping the #DoTheThing group.

Now, let's dig into each conflict point.

TIME AND/OR OTHER PRIORITIES

You have a choice to make. Think back to that timesheet where you wrote down what you want your hero to do more of or less of. Are you willing to use some of those time slots for something that is obviously important enough for your hero to spend time thinking about this way? If so, what?

If you're suddenly saying, "They'll do that someday..." Stop.

How many somedays do they have? Mark your age on this scale. Now, mark the age you plan to do this on the scale.

0---50---100

How do you plan to MAKE time between now and that age to make this happen for your hero? (hint, it's going to involve doing some of the non-mandatory and non-positive things in your time sheet)

Are you worrying about what "people will say" if your hero stops doing the things they have been doing? How important are said "people"? Are they in your hero's Tribe? If not, is your hero willing to give up time, the one thing they cannot make more of, to live up to some random expectation that someone else may or may not have?

Let's ask again...

What are you willing to lose off your hero's schedule that they don't really love and is not mandatory to at least invest in something that they are obviously interested in?

SOMEONE'S JUDGEMENT

At this early stage, you don't actually NEED to share your hero's idea with anyone who is known to be a critical person. We have been surprised to find that the most critical people in our lives who we are afraid to share things with are usually very close to us: parents, siblings, close friends, husbands and wives. Often, they feel like they can predict you and your ordinary world well and are not comfortable with the idea of that world being disrupted.

Other times we are held back by these voices in our heads that came from somewhere. Here is a method we really loved and did a modified version from Julia Cameron's The Artist's Way.

Start writing down lavish praise for why your hero will be awesome at achieving the goal you wrote down as if you were writing them a recommendation letter.

You know, the way you do for others but never for yourself.
Ananya is very good at understanding what humans are struggling with or might be afraid of and helping them overcome it. She is always the one to push people out of the airplane, so to speak. I think the #DoTheThing program will be very useful to many people.

Write yours here

Keep writing. The BEST recommendation you can give for your hero...

Is there a voice of judgement there? Someone wanting to refute this? Someone saying, "they're not that great"?

Whose voice are you hearing? Let's call them The Imaginary Villain. In our sessions, we realized that many times, this is not an actual person, but rather our own voice!

If it is a real person, have they ever said those words to you? What EXACTLY did they say?

Are you worried about what they will say about this idea you have?

What do you think they will say?

Now think back to what people told you they would call on your hero's help for. Write down some of them here. Circle the ones that could help you with your goal.

Were the people who gave you these compliments lying? Do they have any benefit to lying to you?

Do those compliments outnumber the negative statements?

Become your hero's lawyer and refute each point with a statement defending why it will work using the data above from actual witnesses.

So, do you really need to seek the approval of the imaginary villain? Is there a tiny possibility they might be...wrong?

Do you know what that imaginary villain (if a real person) are doing right this second?

Do you think there is a possibility that they don't know or care what you are doing? Are you going to let their theoretical judgement hold you back from something you want to do?

Imaginary Villains are powerful and can lead to some seriously crippling doubt. It's a good thing for all of us to keep in mind when we offer criticism to another person. In doing so unnecessarily, WE might be the voice in their head that's holding them back from reaching their full potential. I never want to be that. Do you?

FEAR

Fear is amazing. Totally psychological, but it paralyzes us. It's one of the greatest forces on earth used to control humans. We are not going to let it hold back your hero though.

What is something your hero is afraid is true about them?

What data do you have to back any of the statements above?

Is this data statistically relevant enough (meaning it came from like 1000 people) to be true?

What is the question your hero is most afraid to be asked?

What is the answer to that question?

What are the chances that anyone is going to ask that today?

Exactly. Let's move on now.

Does your hero have a...

Fear of starting (they don't even know how to start thinking about this)

Fear of what someone else will say (*that* person in their life who will judge them)

Fear of commitment or missing Out (if I spend time on this, I will NOT be spending time on another thing)

Fear of failure (what if it doesn't work and I have wasted my time and energy)

Fear of success (what if I have to choose between this and my current priorities)

Fear of losing something (my life is pretty good, what if I lose something because of this investment)

Fear of something else

If it's any of these fears, the best way to overcome fear is to call it an experiment or learning, not a lifetime commitment. Let's do one now.

LEARNING

If your hero was going to pursue this activity, what is the next step you would advise them to do to learn more about this?

Give your hero permission to be terrible. They are not trying to be the world's great expert. They are trying to learn a tiny bit more than they know now.

Hint: Don't look to experts to learn. Instead look to people who are learning and are just a few steps ahead of you.

Can your hero talk to someone who's done it recently or join an online forum or group or a meetup or a 101 class?

When I wanted to start my own business, I joined a Facebook group called Entrepreneurs Hustle and just loitered, watching the conversation what people talked about. I realized no one knew what they were doing. When I wanted to learn to write a novel, I sat in the back of a writing class for 2 weeks before I brought in anything to read aloud when I realized that many people's writing was not perfect either. When I went to fashion school, I gave myself to be the worst designer in the whole world. Out of 7.4 billion people, I, definitely was going to be the worse at it and that was cool. Doing these things let me off the hook of actually delivering something useful and just turned this into a learning exercise.

What is your hero going to do to learn? A very basic step one.

Yes, it might take you till you're 100 years till you're good at this, but if you don't start today, you're STILL going to be bad tomorrow.

COMPASSION

Think about a time you encouraged someone else when they were blocked or afraid.

Write down the kinds of words you used.

Hey Doug...I am SO proud of you for getting way the heck out of your comfort zone. I know it's scary and hard, but taking this first step is a big deal. Congratulations!

Now cross out their name and write your hero's name and an activity that was challenging for them recently.

Dear Ananya...

How did that feel?

If you're ever feeling imposter-ish, research others who are also early in their phases. What are their stories? Do not choose super-famous people, but rather normal people who are a few steps ahead of you. Realize that these people don't have magic powers...but rather courage.

What's the worst thing that can happen with your hero's idea? That it can fail? You'll be at 0% success? How is that different than now? Think about what a great story this will be. "I had an idea and here is what I did." Vs "I had an idea...and then I did nothing."

People love stories of people who got out of their comfort zones. No one loves (or trusts) "perfect" people who get everything right on a first try. We all know they're putting an Instagram filter on their reality.

Think about how many times you almost drowned while learning to swim, how many scraped knees it took for you to ride a bike, how many times you misspelled "exercise" before getting it right on a spelling test.

You do not get things 100% right on a first or second try. The third, fourth and fifth times are when you truly, TRULY get "the hang" of something.

You already know how to recover from failure. You are a gritty creature. We all know gritty, resilient creatures are the ones who make it to the end. Let's celebrate your grittiness.

Write a letter to the younger version of your hero detailing a spectacular failure they've had and how they recovered. When I did this, it led to me realizing what this book needed to be. You'll find a segment of mine on getting over my fear of public speaking on the next page.

Hey there champ:

This is you from the future paying you a little visit from 2017. Slightly creepy but you'll want to hear this. Remember that Poetry class in college where you had to read something out loud in front of 20 people and you were hyperventilating with nervousness?

Well, many years later, you realized you needed to get over your fear of public speaking and decided to spend the year accepting every speaking gig that came your way. One day someone in college recruiting at Microsoft put out a call for someone to travel to University of Iowa to do a talk to college students on working at Microsoft. You raised your trembling hand for that. Beforehand, you spent one-hour lecturing at the cornfields to practice.

Unfortunately, when you stood on stage staring at the audience...you froze and stumbled through words that made no sense. You got feedback that you're not very good and maybe you should stop. Happily, you decided to give yourself another shot. If you listened to that kind of advice you'd still be contemplating life in the now-closed Goodyear tire factory.

The second time you spoke at a university, you did not freeze, but stumbled through the words. The third time you said the words without stumbling, but shook violently the whole time. The fourth time, you said the words decently, the shaking definitely less. The fifth time you started to enjoy it and realized your nervousness was coming off as energy.

At the end of that year, people were hitting you up for advice on how to speak in public. Now you speak to the public for a living and are able to say words to 5,000 people with only excitement and the desire to share stories (okay the nervousness is there for 5 seconds still) For these things, you followed one simple formula:
1. Do the thing. Don't overthink it, just go for it.
2. If that didn't work (and 99% of the time, it did not) you did the thing AGAIN. That led to actual progress.

It'll take a few tries. Sometimes two, three, four tries, but usually five. Five seems to be your magic number for when you really "get" something. Took you five software jobs to find the one where you're most "you". Five speeches to stop stammer. Try it 5 times.
Love, D

Now write one to your hero:

ACT IV: Do The Thing

This is the part of the story where the hero springs into action. They gather their Tribe. Their find tools. They learn to fight. They #DoTheThing

Think back to your hero's strengths. The things that people call on them for. The things that make them feel powerful and alive. Which of those skills can help with this new adventure?

So, what is step one of what your hero will do to turn these words into action? Once they do step one, step two will naturally show itself. No need to worry about it now. Write step one here.

Now write the activity in a place where your hero will see it often. For me it was a journal screenshot that I set as the lock screen of my phone to always keep it in the forefront of my mind.

How are you going to measure the success of what your hero did? It can be something simple like "they went to the first class and stayed till the end".

What skills do they need to learn (if any) to do this? Remember, they are not getting a PhD in this activity. They are trying it out.

How are and when are they going to do step one? Write it below and put it in the timesheet and mark it as Mandatory because it's mandatory to the commitment you have made to your hero for the past 100 pages. My friend and financial advisor Brandon Erickson says," pay yourself first, then pay the bills." That applies here too. Pay your hero first. They have earned it.

You have a timeframe? Good. Now cross it out and half it. Yes, if it was 3 months, it's now 1.5 months. Don't worry, your hero is strong. They will get it done. They have done greater things than this. Trust me.

Today's date:

Finish step one by:

Now you need to tell someone you trust what you're going to do. Who is going to keep them accountable to making sure they have done it in the halved timeframe? If you don't want to share with anyone in your life, seriously, come tell us in the #DoTheThing group. We keep each other accountable all the time.

Did you tell them?

Go tell them.

Okay, it's time to take that step one. Look at what you wrote down above.

Now let's do it using the 5 second rule. Do the 5 second countdown to yourself. Ready? Say it out loud with me.

You're not saying it. Say it.

5-4-3-2-1 GO.

And that's it!

Congratulations, you survived!

<3

Soooo....what did your hero wind up doing? Did they emerge the hero of this story after all?

Come join us in the #DoTheThing group and let us know how it went. We are always looking for great stories of people who got out of the comfort zone as you have!

Remember you're never alone. You now belong to a global community of people who have heroes who need to get it done. Let's help these heroes #DoTheThing-- together!

I'd love to hear your story for my next week book, whether this process worked for you or not. Please find me at:
Website: http://donasarkar.com
LinkedIn: https://www.linkedin.com/in/donasarkar/
Facebook: https://www.facebook.com/groups/DoTheThingYo/

<3 Dona Sarkar and the #DoTheThing community

Acknowledgements

They say it takes a village to write a book. Well for this one, it took a tribe. Thank you to Aishwarya, Amy, Andrew, Brian, Doug, Fernie, Holly, Ishita, Lachlan, Kasey, Kelly, Kim, Megan, Mike, Pedro, Philippe, Rachel, Rekha, Shane and Subha for the Thursday night gatherings, the stories, the articles and the endless rounds of feedback you were willing to provide. Thank you for being so vulnerable and sharing yourselves with our group. I feel so blessed that you replied to a stranger on the internet and now all of us strangers have become close friends who check in with each other a few times a week to make sure we are still Doing The Thing. I'm so happy you all are the cornerstone of this community.

Kristina Libby: you are my inspiration for someone who fearlessly Does The Thing every single day...and makes it look fun!

My amazing crew: Bambo, Jeremiah, Nikki and Raji, you guys keep me hustling daily to be worthy of being in YOUR tribes. Thank you for the terrible puns, the notorious shenanigans, for picking me up on the bad days and raising me higher on the good. Still !jail.

My wonderful husband Doug Watkins, thank you for being my "step one" guinea pig for this project. You never say no to my notions, whims and fancies. That is a rare and amazing gift. You vowed to me that your greatest success would be seeing me shine. You keep that promise daily. I strive to achieve your levels of patience and kindness every day. Thank you.

Made in the USA
Coppell, TX
05 November 2019